Spring Harv
Bible Workb

Holy Spirit-Filled Life:
A Life Without Limits

Holy Spirit

First published in 2015 by Elevation for Spring Harvest

Elevation is part of Memralife Group, registered charity number 1126997, a company limited by guarantee, registered in England and Wales, number 6667924. 14 Horsted Square, Uckfield, East Sussex, TN22 1QG

ISBN 978-1-899788-97-2

Design by Ascent Creative
Printed by Halcyon

Thank you to Paula Weston, Debbie Shearing, Maddy Carvosso, Peter Lyne and a whole bunch of friends from New Generation who have influenced so much of this workbook.

Contents

About this book 4

Introduction 6

Session 1: Who Is The Holy Spirit? 7

Session 2: Pentecost 12

Session 3: How Can I Be Filled With The Holy Spirit? 17

Session 4: Fruits Of The Holy Spirit 24

Session 5: The Gifts Of The Holy Spirit 28

Session 6: Holy Spirit Working In Us And Through Us 32

Leader's Guide 38

Session 1: Notes - Who Is The Holy Spirit? 42

Session 2: Notes - Pentecost 44

Session 3: Notes - How Can I Be Filled With The Holy Spirit? 46

Session 4: Notes - Fruits Of The Holy Spirit 48

Session 5: Notes - The Gifts Of The Holy Spirit 50

Session 6: Notes - Holy Spirit Working In Us And Through Us 53

Recommended Books For Further Study 55

About this book

This book is written primarily for a group situation, but can easily be used by individuals who want to study The Holy Spirit. It can be used in a variety of contexts, so it is perhaps helpful to spell out the assumptions that we have made about the groups that will use it. These can have a variety of names – homegroups, Bible study groups, cell groups – we've used group as the generic term.

- The emphasis of the studies will be on the application of the Bible. Group members will not just learn facts, but will be encouraged to think 'How does this apply to me? What change does it require of me? What incidents or situations in my life is this relevant to?'

- Groups can encourage honesty and make space for questions and doubts. The aim of the studies is not to find the 'right answer', but to help members understand the Bible by working through their questions. The Christian faith throws up paradoxes. Events in people's lives may make particular verses difficult to understand. The group should be a safe place to express these concerns.

- Groups can give opportunities for deep friendships to develop. Group members will be encouraged to talk about their experiences, feelings, questions, hopes and fears. They will be able to offer one another pastoral support and to get involved in each other's lives.

- There is a difference between being a collection of individuals who happen to meet together every Wednesday and being an effective group who bounce ideas off each other, spark inspiration and creativity, pooling their talents and resources to create solutions together: one whose whole is definitely greater than the sum of its parts. The process of working through these studies will encourage healthy group dynamics.

Space is given for you to write answers, comments, questions and thoughts. This book will not tell you what to think, but will help you discover the truth of God's word through thinking, discussing, praying and listening.

FOR GROUP MEMBERS

- You will probably get more out of the study if you spend some time during the week reading the passage and thinking about the questions. Make a note of anything you don't understand.

- Pray that God will help you to understand the passage and show you how to apply it. Pray for other members in the group too, that they will find the study helpful.

- Be willing to take part in the discussions. The leader of the group is not there as an expert with all the answers. They will want everyone to get involved and share their thoughts and opinions.

- However, don't dominate the group! If you are aware that you are saying a lot, make space for others to contribute. Be sensitive to other group members and aim to be encouraging. If you disagree with someone, say so but without putting down their contribution.

FOR INDIVIDUALS

- Although this book is written with a group in mind, it can also be easily used by individuals. You obviously won't be able to do the group activities suggested, but you can consider how you would answer the questions and write your thoughts in the space provided.

- You may find it helpful to talk to a prayer partner about what you have learnt, and ask them to pray for you as you try and apply what you are learning to your life.

Introduction

"God can do anything, you know — far more than you could ever imagine or guess or request in your wildest dreams! He does it not by pushing us around but by working within us, his Spirit deeply and gently within us".

Ephesians 3:20 The Message

When we encounter God's Holy Spirit, a transformation happens in us and supernatural events begin to happen naturally. Signs and wonders become a normal part of our Christian life. The book of Acts is full of the supernatural power of God. We read about fire appearing in a room, people speaking in tongues, healings and other signs. What a tragedy then, that the church in later years, became responsible for hiding the supernatural dimension of a message that, on the day of Pentecost, was supernaturally preached in multiple languages.

Once the disciples encountered the Holy Spirit they were changed and personally transformed. They were filled with boldness and compassion and became servant leaders.

When we encounter the Holy Spirit, we are given a fresh enthusiasm to tell others about the transformation we've experienced. We want to share our story: "You'll never guess what happened to me...!"

The Bible begins to make sense as the Holy Spirit provides the light to give us understanding as we read Scripture. At Pentecost, Peter suddenly turned into a preacher and Old Testament scholar, interpreting Scripture. He saw 3,000 people saved after preaching. The church was up and running. You can see Acts 2 for the story.

This story is to be continued in us and it all begins with us being transformed by the Holy Spirit. In this study guide we explore who the Holy Spirit is and how we can experience that transformation.

From here, I will be referring to the Holy Spirit without 'the' in his title. Holy Spirit will be his name. I hope this will serve as an encouragement to think about Holy Spirit as a person, knowable and intimate, rather than a vague presence or concept.

Straight From The Heart: David's Story

I was brought up among a group of Christians who took the view that the baptism in the Spirit was for the early Church but not for today.

One year we took our children on holiday to a "Christian" hotel, which turned out to be run by friends of the Pentecostal grouping. They introduced us to their views on the baptism in the Spirit and we heard many speaking in other languages. One evening the preacher invited anyone who wished to receive this baptism to come forward for prayer. I responded and I believe that I then received the baptism. A bit later I was blessed with the ability to speak in another language and, metaphorically speaking, my Christianity dropped from my head to my spirit, opening up the potential for unlimited experience in the spiritual realm. Among other things, I became aware that our gospel is a message of love (rather than condemnation) and that this opens the way for the Holy Spirit to do his work of convicting the unsaved.

As will be obvious, this experience has changed my relationship with our Father and with our Lord Jesus and also led us into the Charismatic Renewal.

To complete the record we returned to this hotel in later years and on one visit my wife received the same blessing. Praise God!

READ THE PASSAGE TOGETHER

[34]Then Peter began to speak: "I now realise how true it is that God does not show favouritism [35]but accepts from every nation the one who fears him and does what is right. [36]You know the message God sent to the people of Israel, announcing the good news of peace through Jesus Christ, who is Lord of all. [37]You know what has happened throughout the province of Judea, beginning in Galilee after the baptism that John preached - [38]how God anointed Jesus of Nazareth with the Holy Spirit and power, and how he went around doing good and healing all who were under the power of the devil, because God was with him.

[39]"We are witnesses of everything he did in the country of the Jews and in Jerusalem. They killed him by hanging him on a cross, [40]but God raised him from the dead on the third day and caused him to be seen. [41]He was not seen by all the people, but by witnesses whom God had already chosen—by us who ate and drank with him after he rose from the dead. [42]He commanded us to preach to the people

and to testify that he is the one whom God appointed as judge of the living and the dead. ⁴³All the prophets testify about him that everyone who believes in him receives forgiveness of sins through his name."

⁴⁴While Peter was still speaking these words, the Holy Spirit came on all who heard the message. ⁴⁵The circumcised believers who had come with Peter were astonished that the gift of the Holy Spirit had been poured out even on Gentiles. ⁴⁶For they heard them speaking in tongues and praising God.

Then Peter said, ⁴⁷"Surely no one can stand in the way of their being baptized with water. They have received the Holy Spirit just as we have." ⁴⁸So he ordered that they be baptized in the name of Jesus Christ. Then they asked Peter to stay with them for a few days.

Acts 10:34-48

Connect

Play 'Who's in the Bag?' or 'Heads Up'.

Creating Space

My thoughts and notes....

What is 'the church' and what is its purpose? Who am I and what is my purpose?

It is impossible to give an answer to questions like these without referring to what we know about Holy Spirit. The birth and growth of the church was through the power of Holy Spirit. We must remember that this is an unfinished story. The baton handed down by the early church is now in our hands and spurs us on to run our lap and take hold of everything our heavenly Father has made available to us - his church.

It seems crazy to think that Jesus would leave his little band of disciples in charge of his master plan - an emerging movement; the church. This was their, and is our, great commission. True, it must have been inspiring to walk the streets alongside Jesus, watching the fulfilment of the

Session 1: Who Is The Holy Spirit?

long-awaited promise prophesied by the prophet Isaiah: 'The blind receive sight, the lame walk, those who have leprosy are cleansed, the deaf hear, the dead are raised, and the good news is proclaimed to the poor.' Matthew 11:5.

Things were just taking off, influence was increasing, courage in the team was growing stronger by the day and then - surely the last thing this group of apprentices needed - their leader disappeared. Just when they were so excited to discover he had indeed been raised from the dead and things were looking better than they could ever have imagined, he very suddenly left them again.

Jesus' departure can only have seemed like a bad idea... *What are we meant to do now?* You can almost hear the team groan! Jesus saw it differently though: 'But very truly I tell you, it is for your good that I am going away. Unless I go away, the Advocate will not come to you; but if I go, I will send him to you.' John 16:7.

Jesus promised to give them Holy Spirit so that the same people who denied and deserted him would be transformed and become fearless in their ability to show and tell the truth that Jesus was alive. They would indeed do the amazing things they had seen him doing, confidently and by the same power. Except, rather than just one who could do these things, now there was a whole crowd of them.

That became good news for you and me.

Who is the Holy Spirit? What does Scripture actually tell us?

Holy Spirit is often called the third person of the Trinity. He is fully God. He is eternal, omniscient and omnipresent. In other words, he is never going to die, he is all-knowing and always present, he is alive and he is a person who speaks (Acts 13:2), has emotions, can be grieved (Ephesians 4:30) and has a will (1 Corinthians 12:11). His ministry and task is to testify and help us testify to the authenticity of Jesus. (John 15:26).

The truth is that Holy Spirit is a person, just as the Father and the Son are. Each of them is distinct from the other and yet identical in essence. Each has a will, loves, and says "I" and "you" when speaking. The Father is not the same person as the Son, who is not the same person as Holy Spirit, who is not the same person as the Father. Each is divine, yet there are not three Gods but one God. (Isaiah 43:10, 44:6-8).

 ## Eat It Up

My thoughts and notes....

Look up these verses and build a picture of Holy Spirit:

Matthew 3:16-17
Matthew 14:16-21
Acts 10:38
2 Peter 1:21
John 3:5
John 14:15-17
John 16:7
John 16:2-14
Romans 8:26-27

Put yourselves in the shoes of the disciples: your leader has gone - how would you have felt?

How would knowing the picture you have just built up, of who Holy Spirit is, have helped the disciples at that time?

Give It Up

Alphabet worship with Alphabet Spaghetti or Scrabble tiles.

Empowered Life

My thoughts and notes....

During the next week why not study some more about Holy Spirit?

Transformation is Holy Spirit's business:

Genesis 1:2 in Creation
Luke 1:35 in Jesus' Birth

How many miracles does the Bible say Jesus did when he was 0-29 years? None!

What or who brought about the change when he reached 30?

Luke 3:22
Luke 4:14

The same Holy Spirit who birthed creation, birthed Jesus and miraculously launched Jesus' ministry, is the same Holy Spirit that Jesus promised would transform the early church - it was a dramatic moment for them, it can also be a dramatic moment for us.

Over The Edge

My thoughts and notes....

Keep a journal of how Holy Spirit prompts you this week. For example: to pray for someone, send a gift to someone, to read a particular passage etc.

Session 2: Pentecost

 ## Straight From The Heart: Avril's Story

I was what is commonly known as a 'cradle Catholic.' I was baptised into the Catholic Church as a baby and brought up by a Catholic mother. I also attended a Catholic convent school and they were very happy years. Despite going to church regularly as I grew up it was very much about rules and duty. I took my faith seriously but felt that God was a very distant God.

When I was about 30 I started to question the existence of God. I was happily married with three young sons but felt that there must be more to life than what I had experienced. I remember clearly asking Mike, my husband, if there really was a God, to which he replied, "Of course! Just look around you at creation." I acknowledged he was right, but if God really existed why didn't I know him? Could I know him? I was really hungry and searching for God.

Then one weekend whilst staying at my mother-in-law's I scanned her bookcase for a book to read and picked out a book called 'Catholic Pentecostals.' I couldn't but the book down. I discovered that you could have a personal relationship with Jesus Christ.

All those years of going to church, hearing the Bible read every Sunday, yet nobody had told me I could really have a close personal and intimate relationship with God. I read about the Holy Spirit and how through the baptism of the Holy Spirit I could powerfully encounter God, experience his presence, and receive and use spiritual gifts. Now I was not only hungry, but ready, open and longing to eat the feast that God had set before me.

Shortly after finishing the book I attended a Catholic charismatic prayer group with great excitement. There I experienced all that I had read about, praise and worship, speaking in tongues, people enthusiastic about the Bible. Soon after that I attended a Catholic Charismatic Renewal day and there I received the experience of the baptism of the Spirit myself.

It was completely different to any experience I had had of church before. Responding to an invitation for prayer, both my son and I found ourselves in the middle of a powerful encounter. I began to pray in tongues (not something I had ever heard in church before) and then witnessed people being miraculously healed as I and others began to pray for them.

My faith truly came alive, the Bible came alive, God's word leapt out at me, it was no longer a dry word but a living vibrant word, and my relationship with God grew and grew and has stayed that way ever since.

It is nearly 30 years since that day and the decision to ask for the baptism of the Holy Spirit is still the most significant decision I made in transforming my faith from religious duty to a life changing encounter with the living God.

READ THE PASSAGE TOGETHER

25"All this I have spoken while still with you. 26But the Advocate, the Holy Spirit, whom the Father will send in my name, will teach you all things and will remind you of everything I have said to you. 27Peace I leave with you; my peace I give you. I do not give to you as the world gives. Do not let your hearts be troubled and do not be afraid.

28"You heard me say, 'I am going away and I am coming back to you.' If you loved me, you would be glad that I am going to the Father, for the Father is greater than I. 29I have told you now before it happens, so that when it does happen you will believe. 30I will not say much more to you, for the prince of this world is coming. He has no hold over me, 31but he comes so that the world may learn that I love the Father and do exactly what my Father has commanded me.

"Come now; let us leave."

John 14:25-31

 Connect

Look together at phrases in some foreign languages – can you translate them?

 Creating Space

My thoughts and notes....

God's rescue plan for the human race wasn't to keep us at arms' length but to send his own Son to close the chasm between us. It doesn't get more up-close and personal than that! Take note that Jesus happily came - the same Jesus who loves to throw stars across the cosmos for us to gaze at in wonder. We're told in the book of John that God so loved the world that he sent his only Son (John 3:16). The Word of God became flesh and blood and moved into our neighbourhood, to become part of our community.

Interestingly, Jesus himself said: "But the Advocate, the Holy Spirit, whom the Father will send in my name, will teach you all things and will remind you of everything I have said to you." (John 14:26); the Holy Spirit was going to be poured out on all people of all ages. We love the Word of God; it's like freshly baked bread to us or a lighthouse on a stormy day. As we enjoy God's word we come to recognise the need for the intervention of Holy Spirit and his engagement in our lives.

Jesus spoke many times about Holy Spirit and used the word *Paraclete* to describe him. This is a Greek word meaning 'a person who helps another person'. Like a lawyer defending your case and standing up for you. But it's free Legal Aid.

Jesus promised the disciples that they were going to benefit from his departure and said that having the Counsellor with them was better than him staying (John 16:7). It may have sounded like a high-risk plan but Jesus was saying Holy Spirit would be able to do far more than the earthly Jesus was able to do. Can you imagine that? A movement of people launched and empowered by the very same passion and influence that hovered over the waters of early creation!

After encountering Holy Spirit, the disciples spread themselves out to the ends of the earth, guided, encouraged and empowered by him.

What the church now calls Pentecost is available to us. Just as Holy Spirit was poured out on the disciples and the Old Testament prophecy in Joel Chapter 2 was fulfilled, the grace and power of God is poured out from this little start-up group we now call the church. What's more, it's available for all of us, even today, even right now.

"They saw what seemed to be tongues of fire that separated and came to rest on each of them" (Acts 2:3).

When Holy Spirit came it wasn't about a nice feeling or sensation; he came as new tongues speaking in new languages to take the story of Jesus around the world. It endowed new boldness to go to the nations of the world.

Holy Spirit generously shares his tools with the church so we can supernaturally get the job done in our world today.

 ## Eat It Up

The Promise
- Joel 2:28-32 Old Testament
- John 14:25-27 New Testament - Jesus' promise
- John 16:7

The 'Clothing'
- Luke 24:49 being filled
- Acts 2:1-13 being filled to overflowing

The Purpose
- Acts 14:8-10 the miraculous
- Acts 8:4-8 deliverance
- Acts 19:1-20 the Kingdom of God

Talk about promises we make in contrast to God's promises. Do we always keep our promises? Does God keep his promises?

What was the impact on the disciples when God's promise to send Holy Spirit was fulfilled?

What is the result for us?

Are there any limits or boundaries to Holy Spirit working in us? Is it possible to remove these boundaries?

Give It Up

Light some candles or a fire, if you are in a safe environment to do so, and meditate on Isaiah 40:25-31.

Empowered Life

My thoughts and notes....

Research when Pentecost is remembered in our calendar. What is another name for it? How could you celebrate Pentecost?

Read Acts 2:37-41.

What do you think the main purpose of Pentecost was and how does this affect your life?

OR

Read about some Pentecost moments:

Acts 2
Acts 4:23-31   ongoing Pentecost
Acts 8:1-25   the Samaritan Pentecost
Acts 10   the Gentile Pentecost
Acts 9:1-19   Paul's Pentecost

Over The Edge

My thoughts and notes....

Ask Holy Spirit for the power to tell your story to someone this week. Record how it goes in your journal.

Session 3: How Can I Be Filled With The Holy Spirit?

 ## Straight From The Heart: Emily's Story

Through a journey of friendship, discovery, questions and experiences, I finally got to the moment of decision: deciding to give myself to God. After some months deliberating whether I believed or not, I knew I could ask no more questions, attend no more prayer gatherings or church meetings, or talk more to those of faith who had become my friends. I had to choose and make my jump. I simply knew I had to decide whether or not I believed in God, for myself, not because my then boyfriend had become a Christian, but because I believed.

Back in February 1999 I had a day off work. I had got to know the church leaders at a local church, where my boyfriend had joined, really well over the past few months. One Sunday I said to Peter, the leader, 'I have the day off work tomorrow, is it ok if I come and see you at the office for a chat?'

That was the day of my decision, say yes or no to God, jump or carry on doing my own thing, which wasn't really going anywhere. I knew I believed and was desperate to know God more, to trust in him and give him my life.

So I met with Peter and, weirdly, his wife Jane happened to be around that day and my boyfriend, John, was free. So it ended up we all met in what was a little meeting room at our community centre.

I did it. I said, 'I want to become a Christian and give my life to Jesus!'

They led me through a prayer, I asked for forgiveness and knew in that moment, I had done it, I had jumped and God was there. Everything seemed different.

Then Jane asked if they could pray for me to baptised in the Holy Spirit. They had already explained about what that was, and over the past few months I had seen Holy Spirit at work in other people. So Jane prayed for me, they laid hands on my head and shoulders. I can't quite describe the feeling, but I know something was happening that wasn't me. Jane said to try speaking, and what came out of my mouth wasn't of my shaping, but strange new sounds and words. I was speaking in tongues!

That day everything changed, it all seemed like a new birthday. Things looked different, words in the Bible jumped off the page. It was good not to hesitate about being baptised in the Holy Spirit. Once you give your life to Jesus, get baptised in the Spirit straight away. Father, Son and Holy Spirit are one and you need them all at the same time.

After that day Peter said, 'I knew, as soon as you asked on that Sunday if you could meet up in the week, that you were going to become a Christian.' I then found out others in church had been praying for me to become a Christian. I chose to believe in God, but he had already been in pursuit of me.

That year, in February I became a Christian and joined the adventure of the church, in June I got engaged and in December we got married. Today I'm still on the adventure with the same church, still married and have two great children. Holy Spirit has had a powerful impact in my life.

READ THE PASSAGE TOGETHER

¹¹From Troas we put out to sea and sailed straight for Samothrace, and the next day we went on to Neapolis. ¹²From there we travelled to Philippi, a Roman colony and the leading city of that district of Macedonia. And we stayed there several days.

¹³On the Sabbath we went outside the city gate to the river, where we expected to find a place of prayer. We sat down and began to speak to the women who had gathered there. ¹⁴One of those listening was a woman from the city of Thyatira named Lydia, a dealer in purple cloth. She was a worshiper of God. The Lord opened her heart to respond to Paul's message. ¹⁵When she and the members of her household were baptised, she invited us to her home. "If you consider me a believer in the Lord," she said, "come and stay at my house." And she persuaded us.

Acts 16:11-15

 # Connect

Play 'Pass the rice relay'.

 # Creating Space

My thoughts and notes....

What turned a wood worker into a miracle worker?

"And the Holy Spirit descended on him in bodily form like a dove. And a voice came from heaven: "You are my Son, whom I love; with you I am well pleased." (Luke 3:22) He was filled with the Holy Spirit (Luke 4:1).

Suddenly, Jesus was full of power. The news spread like wild fire. "Jesus returned to Galilee in the power of the Spirit, and news about him spread through the whole countryside."(Luke 4:14).

Acts 2 paints quite a picture: a tornado tears through a house but no insurance claim is needed; all the residents have fire all over them, but not one of them is burned! Then suddenly, they find themselves out on the streets, giving incredible speeches to people in languages they had never learned. This wasn't about their ability but about the transforming power of Holy Spirit. This is what happens when God's promises are fulfilled. It gives a whole new meaning to *Fire Exit*!

Don't you think that if Jesus and his apostolic team needed the Holy Spirit and Holy Spirit was there when God was forming the universe, it would be a little unfair to ask us to carry on the work without the same power? Without Holy Spirit life, the Christian faith is simply a bunch of well-meaning people trying to get their act together.

As we said in Session One, God's story is to be continued, the baton is passed to us, and we need to be transformed, just as the early church were, by Holy Spirit.

Let's not worry about exactly when or how someone is filled with Holy Spirit. The real question here is are we full? Ephesians 5:18 says, "Do not get drunk on wine, which leads to debauchery. Instead, be filled with the Spirit". In Greek it is clearly a continuous filling.

"So I say to you: Ask and it will be given to you; seek and you will find; knock and the door will be opened to you. For everyone who asks receives; the one who seeks finds; and to the one who knocks, the door will be opened.

Which of you fathers, if your son asks for a fish, will give him a snake instead? Or if he asks for an egg, will give him a scorpion? If you then, though you are evil, know how to give good gifts to your children, how much more will your Father in heaven give the Holy Spirit to those who ask him!" Luke 11:9-13.

The book of Acts is a journey to be part of, not a story to listen to. Ask yourself: Am I on the journey and am I still moving in the right direction? The story will continue but where am I on the map? Do I know Jesus is alive? Am I filled with Holy Spirit?

As Christians, we often focus on salvation as the end goal - resulting in eternity with Jesus. But God never intended us to stop there - salvation was only ever intended to be the beginning. Jesus is changing us into his likeness and we are a work in progress. In Ephesians 3:19 we read that God's intention for us is to be *"filled with all the fullness of God"*. When we carry the fullness of God we can release the Kingdom of God around us. What we are filled with will be what comes out of us and fills the Earth. When the presence of God, Holy Spirit, fills us, it is for us to let him overflow into the needy world around us.

It's amazing to know we can be continually filled by Holy Spirit, spilling out of us and influencing our surroundings. At any point in our busy day we can be filled afresh. Peter told us, in Acts 2:38, "Repent and be baptised, every one of you, in the name of Jesus Christ for the forgiveness of your sins. And you will receive the gift of the Holy Spirit." So we know Holy Spirit is given to each of us, but Paul in Ephesians takes it even further and says "be filled" using the Greek word meaning "continue being filled".

There are things in our lives that can hinder us from being filled with Holy Spirit. A point that Peter emphasises is how important it is to repent and be baptised. When we turn away from sin - harsh words, foolish thoughts and complaining - we make room in our hearts for Holy Spirit to fill us and dwell there. When we choose thankfulness instead of complaining, forgiveness instead of holding offence, grace instead of judgement, we can invite him to stay there.

Holy Spirit is often represented in the image of a dove. Doves are shy creatures, easily scared away; you wouldn't expect one to stay next to you if you were shouting. In a similar sort of way it would be amazing to be mindful of Holy Spirit with us and watch our mouths and actions. He is, after all, HOLY Spirit.

We all receive Holy Spirit at the point of salvation. However, in addition, we all need to know the reality of the power of the Holy Spirit in our lives. For some, this realisation and appropriation happens gradually. But for many, there needs to be a 'Pentecost moment' when we experience for ourselves what it means to baptised and filled with God's Holy Spirit.

In the book of John, the resurrected Jesus breathes on the disciples and says, "Receive the Holy Spirit."(John 20:22). We then read in Acts that they have their Pentecost moment and are filled. In Acts 19:1-2, Paul asks the Jesus converts, "When you put your faith in Jesus were you given the Holy Spirit?" "No," they answered, "we have never even heard of the Holy Spirit." Needless to say the Holy Spirit was then given to them. Paul made sure that was sorted out. If he were here now he'd do the same for you.

 ## Eat It Up

My thoughts and notes....

Look up these verses together and ask yourself: Have I encountered Holy Spirit for myself in this way? Would I like to?

Receiving the fullness of God
- Ephesians 5:18-20
- Ephesians 3:19

Be baptised and filled
- John 20:19-23
- Acts 1:4-8

Transformed community life
- Acts 2:37-47

Do not quench the Spirit
- 1 Thessalonians 5:19

How has your life changed since the moment of your salvation?

Have you ever experienced being filled/baptised with the Holy Spirit. Would you say you have had a Pentecost moment?

Are there areas of your life that are hidden from God hindering the fullness of his filling?

Give It Up

Everyone write on balloons words the Bible uses to describe God – or even words that you would like to use to describe God, and throw them around. When you catch a balloon shout out the name and what it means to you.

Empowered Life

My thoughts and notes....

Ask to be filled everyday. As Holy Spirit leaks out around you, it's good to keep being re-filled. Read and meditate on these:

John 7:37-39   Come and drink
Nehemiah 8:10   Nehemiah talks about joy
Acts 13:52   Disciples are filled with joy

Ask Holy Spirit to bring you joy and start to laugh!

This week, research past or current revivals/revivalists. For example: The Azusa Street Revival, the Moravian Revival, the Welsh Revival of 1906, Heidi Baker, Smith Wigglesworth, Billy Graham or Charles Finney.

A good resource is a book entitled *God's Generals* by Roberts Liardon or *When God Breaks In* by Michael Green.

Session 4: Fruits Of The Holy Spirit

 ## Straight From The Heart: Katy's Story

Katy had been brought up with revenge. Her dad had left home when she was little and each weekend her mum would load the kids into the car equipped with hammers and knives – drive to her dad's house and pound the door until the police were called. She dealt with every relationship the same way, resulting in great rifts in the family.

Katy's long term partner had had an affair and Katy felt so broken and angry she tried everything she could think of to help – medication, counselling, psychics … nothing helped until a friend suggested she try Alpha. While attending the Alpha course at a local church she decided to give her life to Jesus. She felt Jesus' love fill her but she was still so angry especially with her ex-friend who had seduced her partner.

At Alpha she had been prayed for to receive the Holy Spirit so instead of anger and hate, she would know the fruits of the Spirit. But she couldn't let go of the anger. Parking the car at the local supermarket and arguing over the affair, yet again, on her car phone with her partner, she suddenly saw her ex-friend walking in front of the car. She told her partner and hung up. All the anger in her welled up and she drove the car full speed towards this woman with the intention of running her down. Suddenly, instead being overcome with anger, she was filled with love for her friend and screeched the car to a stop inches from impact. She jumped out of the car and ran around to talk to her. By the time she got back in the car there were over 30 missed calls from her partner. She called him back and he answered the phone in tears. Expecting the worst, knowing Katy's normal behaviour, he asked what she had done. He couldn't believe that everything was ok.

Katy called me a week later. Her mum was really cross with her as Katy, with her new found fruits of the Spirit growing in her, was daily restoring relationships with family and friends that she and her family had fought with for years.

In spite of her mother's misgivings, Katy had never felt so at peace.

READ THE PASSAGE TOGETHER

²²But the fruit of the Spirit is love, joy, peace, forbearance, kindness, goodness, faithfulness, ²³gentleness and self-control. Against such things there is no law. ²⁴Those who belong to Christ Jesus have crucified the flesh with its passions and desires. ²⁵Since we live by the Spirit, let us keep in step with the Spirit. ²⁶Let us not become conceited, provoking and envying each other.

Galatians 5:22-26

 Connect

'Guess the fruit' from taste only.

 Creating Space

My thoughts and notes....

When you gave your life to Jesus, Holy Spirit planted the fruits of the Spirit inside you. They were planted as a seed and have the potential to grow into massive fruits.

When Holy Spirit fills us, we find that things do not stay the same. When the Spirit hovered over the waters, he brought order, creation, growth and sustainment to what looked like utter chaos and carnage. Things grew; they matured and multiplied. Likewise when Holy Spirit fills us, something creative begins to happen. Fruits are grown and gifts are birthed.

It is part of our transformation.

A tree that has no nourishment and is not firmly rooted will not bear fruit. Fruit does not appear on a tree overnight. But there is some establishing of roots, pruning of branches, maturing of the trunk and Son light (Did you notice that?). We need to be firmly rooted in the Word of God, receiving nourishment from his Word and Spirit and definitely getting lots of the Son... in order for the fruit in our lives to grow and be good.

When Holy Spirit fills us, things happen; shoots appear, blossoms bud, leaves unfurl and fruits flourish. Fruit such as kindness, goodness and self-control begin to grow as a result of the filling. We then have a responsibility to keep moving forward by using those fruits, with Holy Spirit enabling us to continue to grow them within us. We start to look different on the outside.

The seeds of the fruit of the Spirit are best grown with the nutrient called 'loads of love'. When we get this ingredient right it's easy for the seeds to grow without us even trying.

The more we allow Holy Spirit to fill us, the more we can let go of some of the barriers and controls that can often hold us back from living life to the full. The more we do this, the more fruit is grown in us and released around us. You may find you have more patience. You may find you have more joy. You may find that things that offended you before can now just be brushed off.

 ## Eat It Up

My thoughts and notes....

Galatians 5:25   Whose leading do we follow?
Ephesians 5:7-9   How should we live and why?

Can you list the fruits of the Spirit?

Check out these verses:
- Galatians 5:22-23   Some of the fruits
- 1 Corinthians 13:4 - 8 Love
- Hebrews 12:2   Joy
- Romans 15:13   Peace and Hope
- Ephesians 4:2   Patience (longsuffering)
- 2 Corinthians 6:6-7   Kindness
- Ephesians 5:9   Goodness
- Ephesians 3:16-17   Faith
- Ephesians 4:2   Meekness
- 2 Peter 1:5-7   Self Control

How are they growing for you?

Give It Up

Think of something you are grateful to God for and write it on a note. Make a gratitude wall with post-it notes.

Empowered Life

My thoughts and notes....

Why not do a Bible study to find what God says about love, especially God's love for you. Perhaps write verses down to stick on walls in your home, or put them on your phone home screen and keep saying them over yourself.

Once we get the revelation of how much God loves us, we can love ourselves. It is difficult to love other people if we don't love ourselves.

(It might be good to start with the definition of love in 1 Corinthians 13.)

Over The Edge

My thoughts and notes....

It's amazing what can happen when we make the decision to love.

Discuss the idea of 'Pay it forward', and showing love to someone this week.

('Pay it forward' means to do good deeds for others without expecting anything in return. For example, buy someone's coffee, pay the bill for the person behind you, pay for somebody's parking or help someone clean their house etc.)

Continue the gratitude wall at home or use a mirror as a place to stick your messages of thanks. Perhaps include what God says about how much he loves you, too.

Session 5: The Gifts Of The Holy Spirit

 ## Straight From The Heart: Sally's Story

I grew up in a church that, although not 'strict', had strict roots. The gifts of the Spirit were not preached a great deal and I had never really thought the gifts of the Spirit were for nowadays. I also hadn't thought about having any of the gifts myself - aside from teaching.

A few years ago I moved to another church with my husband, a very different church to the one I had come from. I'd never heard speaking in tongues and when I heard it at this new church I was very uncomfortable and had to leave the meeting. This happened several times. Then, over time, God graciously helped me to open up a bit, and I started to feel more at home with the style of worship there and their expectation for the Holy Spirit to work.

Over time I have come to realise the Holy Spirit can and does work through us with these gifts. Some things I did know about, but under a different name - the gift of prophecy I would have called having 'a word from the Lord.' I am more open now to the Holy Spirit and his work, and even prophesied at our community group meeting - but I still think of it as a word from the Lord! I really feel this is how the Holy Spirit has worked in me - coming from a place where I didn't believe his gifts were real to being able to see him at work in my life through them.

READ THE PASSAGE TOGETHER

[27]Now you are the body of Christ, and each one of you is a part of it. [28]And God has placed in the church first of all apostles, second prophets, third teachers, then miracles, then gifts of healing, of helping, of guidance, and of different kinds of tongues. [29]Are all apostles? Are all prophets? Are all teachers? Do all work miracles? [30]Do all have gifts of healing? Do all speak in tongues? Do all interpret? [31]Now eagerly desire the greater gifts. And yet I will show you the most excellent way.

1 Corinthians 12:27-31

 **Connect**

Play 'Pass The Parcel'.

Creating Space

God is a giving God and loves to give to his children. All that we receive is because of God's love and kindness to us. He is a good God and a loving Father. It is because of God's love for you and me that he gives us the ultimate gift of Jesus, his Son. When we really understand his love for us, we are able to love, both ourselves and the world around us. It is this love, both for us and through us, that remains most important. We cannot earn his love, it is given by grace.

The word 'Charismata' is used in the Bible for any grace gifts, i.e. gifts that are undeserved. This is God's heart and goodness for us. This word is used to talk about any good gifts that come from God, such as: deliverance, prayers, marriage, and celibacy. It is also used to talk about eternal gifts, the gift of life, salvation, and forgiveness. In Corinthians it is used to describe the gifts given to us by Holy Spirit.

The gifts of Holy Spirit are available to all who have been filled. Paul in Corinthians urges us to eagerly desire them, but reminds us we cannot earn them. Gifts are given in response to our desire. They are handed out with a big portion of grace to handle that gift. As you function and try it out, so the gift enlarges so we might use them to help the church become the best representation of Jesus' bride and the best window for the world to view what the church is all about.

Just as God's motive to send his Son is love, the most important gift Holy Spirit gives us is love.

A love that permeates our lives and then also the world around us.

Gifts of the Spirit:
 - 1 Corinthians 12:7-11
 - 1 Corinthians 14:1

The gifts Holy Spirit gives you will affect not only your life but equip the church and help to reach the lost.

Eat It Up

My thoughts and notes....

Can you name gifts of the Spirit and their purposes?

Have you experienced any of the gifts of the Holy Spirit?

Can they be developed, and if so how?

Give It Up

Shout Outs - Shout out what you are thankful to God for when you consider the people around you.

Empowered Life

My thoughts and notes....

Look at these verses for further study into the gifts available to us. Then, begin to write down the gifts you think you do have and the gifts you would like to have. Remember God said, "Ask and it will be given to you" (Matthew 7:7).

Isaiah 11:2-3
Ephesians 4:11
Romans 12:6-8
1 Peter 4:10-11
1 Timothy 4:14

Put all your names in a hat. Each person then picks out a name to take away. The idea is that you pray for that person and write something for them - a prophecy, an encouraging, exalting or comforting word. Bring it to the next session and share it with everyone.

Session 6: Holy Spirit Working In Us And Through Us

Straight From The Heart: Luke's Story

Having grown up in a Christian home, Jesus wasn't new to me at all. I just viewed him a bit like royalty - I believed he was real and I knew people who had encountered him, but for me on a personal level, there wasn't much to report. When I was 12, my mum ended up meeting a bunch of Spirit-filled Catholics who gave her a book about the Holy Spirit. By the time the book was finished, we had had loads of conversations about whether an encounter with the Holy Spirit was in reach for us too. Going to a church gathering expecting to experience God was a new concept, but what happened to me the first time I did, has left its mark.

Unbeknownst to me, at the very same meeting where I had gone to find out if I could be filled with the Holy Spirit, another lady was there who felt God had told her she was going to be prayed for by a child and be healed from a severe back injury. It was an injury so bad that at times she would have to lie on the floor for days at a time. When the time came, I responded to an invitation to receive the Holy Spirit. As people prayed for me I felt an overwhelming sense of peace and unexpectedly started to speak in a language I didn't understand (I know now it was the gift of tongues). Before I could stop the woman and explain I didn't know what I was doing, she started inviting people who were sick to come for prayer and told them I was going to pray for them. Of course the lady with the back injury was first in line and to my absolute shock was instantly healed in front of my eyes. She stayed that way for the many years during which I stayed in touch with her. I also ended up praying for a lady whose fingers were curled up with Arthritis. Once again, to my (and my mum's) surprise, her fingers completely straightened in front of our eyes and stayed straight – this was something that hadn't happened for years. I was so overwhelmed by the whole experience that when I went back to school after the weekend I couldn't stop talking about what had happened. I ended up taking an RE lesson about how to be filled with the Holy Spirit. The summary of the lesson was simple – just ask...

READ THE PASSAGE TOGETHER

⁶Paul and his companions travelled throughout the region of Phrygia and Galatia, having been kept by the Holy Spirit from preaching the word in the province of Asia. ⁷When they came to the border of Mysia, they tried to enter Bithynia, but the Spirit of Jesus would not allow them to. ⁸So they passed by Mysia and went down to Troas. ⁹During the night Paul had a vision of a man of Macedonia standing and begging

him, "Come over to Macedonia and help us." [10]After Paul had seen the vision, we got ready at once to leave for Macedonia, concluding that God had called us to preach the gospel to them.

Acts 16:6-10

Connect

Play the Blindfold Shape Drawing Challenge.

Creating Space

My thoughts and notes....

Collins English Dictionary describes 'supernatural' as 'occurrences and things that cannot be explained by science.'

Holy Spirit engages with us to give us power and endurance that we might run the race and keep on running it with vitality. In the book of Acts, Holy Spirit filled the disciples with power and the church exploded on to the scene.

Holy Spirit loves the church and gives us gifts, for free, to exercise. Through those gifts the whole body is joined and held together, every supporting ligament strengthened and grown, being built up in love as each part does its work.

As the fruit grows in us and we develop the gifts given to us, Holy Spirit helps us to be humble and gentle. It means being patient and bearing with one another in love, honouring each other and maintaining unity in the body of Christ.

Pentecostal televangelist Oral Roberts says: "The atmosphere of expectancy is the breeding ground for miracles."

What if our expectation was to live our lives experiencing God's supernatural involvement? Imagine if our faith was resting on God's power and not on human wisdom? When the answer is yes, the supernatural becomes supernaturally normal.

Jesus knew who he was; he had expectation. Just look at his mission statement from Isaiah 61 quoted in Luke 4:18-19.

Jesus healed the sick. At his word the paralysed walked, storms were calmed, and the hungry were fed. He walked on water, raised the dead and cast out demons.

Jesus has given us the great commission (Matthew 28:19-20) and told us we will see and do even greater things than he did (John 14:12). It's Holy Spirit who breaks the supernatural into our natural. It's through Jesus, and in the power of Holy Spirit, that we can also 'do' miracles, as we see in John 20:30-31.

When we learn to walk with Holy Spirit, allowing the supernatural to become natural, our lives will never be the same. We will be living in the fullness of joy.

Jesus was building a supernatural community, a church of God's people displaying God's power. A body with many parts, full of love, empowered by the filling of Holy Spirit. So how about actively allowing and asking him to fill us and keep on filling us?

Then, step out of the known into the unknown, out of the natural into the supernatural, or as Peter was asked: 'Step out of the boat!' (Matthew 14:29)

In John 4:4-26, Jesus uses spiritual gifts and tells a woman, who he had never met before, her life story. It provokes a revival.

In John 9:1-41, in a very unconventional way, Jesus heals a man born blind (using spit and the dust he was standing on).

These are amazing stories; imagine one of these same stories happening in the cinema, pub, nightclub, shopping centre, or your gym. It could be you! Dare to change the way you think - go outside the box; don't put Holy Spirit in a mould.

In John 14:12 Jesus says anyone who has faith in him will do even greater things – in fact more than we could hope or imagine. Wow – are you up for that?

Encounters with Holy Spirit lead us to Jesus and show us who the Father is so that we can fall more in love with him. As you pursue gifts from Holy Spirit that are available to you, press into the Bible and you will discover a whole new love relationship with Jesus; one that is totally life transforming, one that will have us all looking more and more like Jesus. Who wouldn't want that?

Eat It Up

Would you like to see these things in your life?

What do you think hinders you from experiencing a totally supernaturally natural lifestyle?

What's one thing you might consider doing to change your natural into the supernatural?

Acts of Compassion
- Matthew 14:14   Healing many
- Mark 1:41   Healing a man with leprosy

Works of Protest Against Evil
- Mark 5:36-43   Raising Jairus' Daughter
- Mark 8:22-26   Healing a blind man at Bethsaida
- Mark 7:31-37   Healing a deaf and dumb man
- Mark 4:39   Calming the storm

Acts of Faith
- Matthew 17:27   Money appearing
- John 2:1-11   Turning water into wine
- Matthew 14:22-33   Walking on water
- Matthew 14:13-21   Feeding thousands

Give It Up

Write a letter to God. Allow yourself time to write down your deepest dreams and desires.

Empowered Life

My thoughts and notes....

Look up some of the supernatural events Jesus did and start to ask Holy Spirit to use you, that you may begin to see the same, and more.

Supernatural events in the New Testament:
- Acts 3:6   The crippled beggar being healed
- Acts 8:26   Philip transported in the Spirit
- Acts 5:12   Signs and Wonders
- Acts 8:7   Demons cast out
- Acts 10:30   Angels appear
- Acts 12:6-10 Peter's escape from prison
- Acts 16:9   Paul's vision
- Acts 19:11   Extraordinary miracles
- Acts 20:10   Paul raises Eutychus from the dead
- Acts 28:3-5 Paul protected from a snake bite
- Acts 28:9   Sick people on Malta were healed

Over The Edge

My thoughts and notes....

Ask the Holy Spirit to guide you specifically this week, and expect to see his power at work in you and through you. Don't forget to keep a journal of your journey!

Leader's Guide

TO HELP YOU LEAD

You may have led a group many times before or this may be your first time. Here is some advice on how to lead these studies.

- As a group leader, you don't have to be an expert or a lecturer. You are there to facilitate the learning of the group members – helping them to discover for themselves the wisdom in God's word. You should not be doing most of the talking or dishing out the answers, whatever the group expects from you!

- You do need to be aware of the group's dynamics, however. People can be quite quick to label themselves and each other in a group situation. One person might be seen as the expert, another the moaner who always has something to complain about. One person may be labelled as quiet and not expected to contribute; another person may always jump in with something to say. Be aware of the different type of individuals in the group, but don't allow the labels to stick. You may need to encourage those who find it hard to get a word in, and quieten down those who always have something to say. Talk to members between sessions to find out how they feel about the group.

- The sessions are planned to try and engage every member in active learning. Of course you cannot force anyone to take part if they don't want to, but it won't be too easy to be a spectator. Activities that ask everyone to write down a word, or talk in twos and then report back to the group are there for a reason. They give everyone space to think and form their opinion, even if not everyone voices it out loud.

- Do adapt the sessions for your group as you feel is appropriate. Some groups may know each other very well and will be prepared to talk at a deep level. New groups may take a bit of time to get to know each other before making themselves vulnerable, but encourage members to share their lives with each other.

- You probably won't be able to tackle all the questions in each session so decide in advance which ones are most appropriate to your group and situation.

- Encourage a number of replies to each question. The study is not about finding a single right answer, but about sharing experiences and thoughts in order to find out how to apply the Bible to people's lives. When brainstorming, don't be too quick to evaluate the contributions. Write everything down and then have a look to see which suggestions are worth keeping.

- Similarly, encourage everyone to ask questions, voice doubts and discuss difficulties. Some parts of the Bible are difficult to understand. Sometimes the Christian faith throws up paradoxes. Painful things happen to us that make it difficult to see what God is doing. A group should be a safe place to express all of this. If discussion doesn't resolve the issue, send everyone away to pray about it between sessions, and ask your minister for advice.

- Give yourself time in the week to read through the Bible passage and the questions. Read the Leaders' notes for the session, as different ways of presenting the questions are sometimes suggested. However during the session don't be too quick to come in with the answer – sometimes people need space to think.

- Delegate as much as you like! The easiest activities to delegate are reading the text, and the worship sessions, but there are other ways to involve the group members. Giving people responsibility can help them own the session much more.

- Pray for group members by name, that God would meet with them during the week. Pray for the group session, for a constructive and helpful time. Ask the Lord to equip you as you lead the group.

THE STRUCTURE OF EACH SESSION

Feedback: find out what people remember from the previous session, or if they have been able to act during the week on what was discussed last time.

Bible reading: it's important actually to read the passage you are studying during the session. Ask someone to prepare this in advance or go around the group reading a verse or two each. Don't assume everyone will be happy to read out loud.

Questions and activities: adapt these as appropriate to your group. Some groups may enjoy a more activity-based approach; some may prefer just to discuss the questions. Try out some new things!

Worship: suggestions for creative worship and prayer are included, which give everyone an opportunity to respond to God, largely individually. Use these alongside singing or other group expressions of worship. Add a prayer time with opportunities to pray for group members and their families and friends.

Further study: suggestions are given for those people who want to study the themes further. These could be included in the group if you feel it's appropriate and if there is time.

WHAT YOU NEED

A list of materials that are needed is printed in each session in the Leaders' Guide. In addition you will probably need:

Bibles: the main Bible passage is printed in the book so that all the members can work from the same version. It is useful to have other Bibles available, or to ask everyone to bring their own, so that other passages can be referred to.

Paper and pens: for people who need more space than is in the book!

Flip chart: it is helpful to write down people's comments during a brainstorming session, so that none of the suggestions is lost. There may not be space for a proper flip chart in the average lounge, and having one may make it feel too much like a business meeting or lecture. Try getting someone to write on a big sheet of paper on the floor or coffee table, and then stick this up on the wall with blu-tack.

GROUND RULES

How do people know what is expected of them in a group situation? Is it ever discussed, or do we just pick up clues from each other? You may find it helpful to discuss some ground rules for the group at the start of this course, even if your group has been going a long time. This also gives you an opportunity to talk about how you, as the leader, see the group. Ask everyone to think about what they want to get out of the course. How do they want the group to work? What values do they want to be part of the group's experience; honesty, respect, confidentiality? How do they want their contributions to be treated? You could ask everyone to write down three ground rules on slips of paper and put them in a bowl. Pass the bowl around the group. Each person takes out a rule and reads it, and someone collates the list. Discuss the ground rules that have been suggested and come up with a top five. This method enables everyone to contribute fairly anonymously. Alternatively, if your group are all quite vocal, have a straight discussion about it!

NB Not all questions in each session are covered, some are self-explanatory.

ICONS

 Straight From The Heart - Each session starts with a true story to set the context of the chapter, and a suggested Bible passage to put the story in the context of the teaching of Scripture. Feel free to tell your own story or experience that relates to the topic.

 Connect - An ice breaker or starter activity. A time for the group to connect together.

 Creating Space - Some thought and general questions provide a platform to look at the subject material together.

 Eat It Up - Discuss and digest what you have just read and let it go deeper. This contains extra Bible verses, an activity or further questions. You might want to break the group into groups of twos or threes to talk together.

 Give It Up - Time to focus on God through different types of worship.

 Empowered Life - Further study that can be completed during the week.

 Over The Edge - A challenge to put your learning into action during the week.

Session 1: Notes - Who Is The Holy Spirit?

Bible Passage: Acts 10:34-48
It's helpful for each member of the group to have a Bible as well as a workbook.

 **Connect**

Play 'Who's in the Bag?' or 'Heads Up'.

You will need paper and pens, hat/bowl or Heads Up App

How to play:

Everyone is given five strips of paper and a pen. Each person, in secret, writes the names of five famous people (they could be a singer, actor, sports player, fictional character etc.) Once everyone has written down their five names, the papers are folded up separately and all put into the hat. The group is divided into two teams who compete against each other. A volunteer from the first team pulls a piece of paper out of the hat. The aim is to describe the famous person on the paper without using any part of the person's name. Once it has been correctly guessed by their team members, the volunteer pulls out another piece of paper and the aim is to complete as many as possible in 60 seconds. Then it is the other team's turn. This continues until all the names from the hat have been guessed. Then the moment of truth: count up how many each team guessed correctly and see who has won.

Example: David Beckham - Possible description without using his name: played football for England and Manchester United. Married to a Spice Girl. Underwear model. (Keep describing him until they guess his name.)

Alternatively, you could play 'Heads Up'.

'Heads Up' is an app that can be downloaded on any iPad or smartphone – download this beforehand and acquaint yourself with it. Or you could prepare the clues to play a round of Charades.

Eat It Up

Encourage the group to build up a picture of Holy Spirit.

Divide into pairs and give each pair a Scripture or two (you could have typed slips ready as they may not have Bibles with them). Get them to discuss what aspect of Holy Spirit's personality is revealed and then share with the rest of the group when they come back together. Perhaps draw and write on a board/flipchart to begin to build a fuller picture.

Give It Up

Alphabet worship with Alphabet Spaghetti or Scrabble tiles.

You will need:
A can of Alphabet Spaghetti or a bag of Scrabble tiles.
Forks
Plate

Pass the can or bag around and, in turn, people hook out a letter. Think of a word to describe God starting with that letter.

Alternatively, you can go around the group using the letters of the alphabet. For example:

A = Almighty, B = Beautiful, C = Compassionate, D = Dedicated etc.

Session 2: Notes - Pentecost

Bible Passage: John 14:25-31
It's helpful for each member of the group to have a Bible as well as a workbook.

Connect

In advance, using 'Google Translate', write out phrases in a foreign language.
(Don't forget to write yourself a separate piece of paper with the English versions!)
Bible verses can be used if you like. Let people guess what the phrases say.

Creating Space

You may want to read about Pentecost in Acts 2:1-13 before leading the session.

Pentecost fulfilled Jesus' promise to send a Counsellor and Spirit of Truth.
It marks the day the Holy Spirit fell on the Apostles.
Pentecost is known as the birth day of the church.

Way back in the Old Testament Joel promised the coming of Holy Spirit
(Joel 2:28-29). The church is a prophetic people on a prophetic journey.
A prophetic journey that was actually commissioned in the Garden of Eden when
God said, "Go forth and multiply" (Genesis 9:7). This moment, at Pentecost,
where Holy Spirit was poured out, marked an important moment in this prophetic
journey and an important moment for us, as we continue the prophetic journey.

Eat It Up

Look through the following verses and see how Holy Spirit was promised, came at
Pentecost and the effect afterwards on the disciples and their journey.

Sometimes we don't understand the circumstances we find ourselves in, just like
the disciples didn't understand Jesus when he said he was going to leave them.
However, we have God's Word to hold on to and his promises, which we can be
assured he will stick to. So even in turbulent waters, we can trust in God.

Give It Up

You may want a good reader to read the passage Isaiah 40:25-31 aloud a few times.

Over The Edge

You might want to encourage people to write down their testimony so it can be told in a few minutes. Or perhaps a story about something Jesus has done for them such as a healing. Think about how this can be told to someone who does not know Jesus.

Session 3: Notes - How Can I Be Filled With The Holy Spirit?

Bible Passage: Acts 16:11-15
It's helpful for each member of the group to have a Bible as well as a workbook.

 Connect

Play 'Pass the rice relay'.

You will need:
2 spoons
Rice (You could also use water, or anything else you like.)
4 containers

Divide your group into two teams and have each team line up. At the head of each line place a container with rice in it, and a spoon. Put an empty container at the end of each line. On your signal, each leader fills their spoon with rice and passes it to the next player. Pass it all the way down the line and empty what is left on the spoon into the container. The last person in the line who now has the spoon runs to the front and begins the process again until every player has been at the head of the line. The winning team is the one with the most rice in their once empty container.

To make it more difficult, you could insist that players alternately pass the spoon under their legs and over their heads.

Creating Space

How do I get filled up? You may want to do a physical demonstration to explain this: Ask someone to pass a glass of water. Then decide whether to take it or not.

Explain: There are two things that would prevent me from having that water; not asking and not receiving. That's how you are filled, you ask and receive. The two go together, hand-in-hand.

Eat It Up

You may want to pray for each other to be filled (baptised) with the Holy Spirit at this moment. (This doesn't mean you haven't had the Spirit up till now – but this is about receiving everything God has got for you!) It may be helpful for you to consider, before leading the group and praying for one another, possible manifestations of the Holy Spirit if this is new to you or them.

Sometimes there is nothing visible on the outside, but people have had a powerful encounter. Outward manifestations are not a measure as to whether someone has been filled or not, although they are common. Sometimes people fall over as either Holy Spirit has overwhelmed them or maybe because Holy Spirit wants to minister to them. Sometimes people will shake or cry or laugh or groan. These manifestations can look scary but I have yet to meet anyone who hasn't wanted more afterwards.

Some years ago, my wife's back was healed and without anyone even praying for her she fell backwards on the ground and lay for an hour shaking violently. She thought it had only been five minutes and when she got up she was totally healed.

I think it's best not to put Holy Spirit in a box and limit what he should or shouldn't do and how people should or shouldn't react, but just allow Holy Spirit to take care of it. (Some people may be so affected by Holy Spirit that they may not want to continue with the next activity so allow them to continue enjoying God).

Give It Up

You will need: Balloons, marker pens, music

Set the scene: Create a party/celebration atmosphere.

You may want to put some lively music on and have some blowers and streamers. You could even get out some pots and pans and wooden spoons to create your own drum beats. It's good to get those who are able to move about instead of sitting down, as this helps to bring freedom and encourages us to be less self-conscious.

As you do this you might want to pray for joy over each other.

Session 4: Notes - Fruits Of The Holy Spirit

Bible Passage: Galatians 5:22-26
It's helpful for each member of the group to have a Bible as well as a workbook.

Connect

You will need:
Exotic fruit and other food for taste test
Blindfold

Get a variety of exotic fruits and have some cut up ready. Get people to take it in turns to be blindfolded. They then need to guess what you are feeding them.

You could add a few unexpected things to make it more difficult! Check about allergies before you begin.

Eat It Up

You may want to give people a verse each, or get them to look up the passages in their Bibles, in pairs, and then share with the group.

Ask people to think about this question:
How are they growing for you?

Having unforgiveness in our hearts, or holding on to offence, can be a barrier to Holy Spirit. If people feel there is a blockage, it may be worth them asking God to show them if there is anyone they need to forgive. It is not by struggling we are filled, but by surrendering to Jesus. Sometimes fear gets in the way. The Bible says, "Perfect love casts out fear" (1 John 4:18). We need to know God's love for us. In Psalms it says, "God follows us every day of our lives with goodness and mercy" (Psalm 23:6). He wants good things for us. He's a good Dad.

James 3:14 -17 tells us we need to keep our hearts pure.

Jesus said if we abide in him we will produce spiritual fruit in our lives.

Give It Up

You will need:
Post-it notes and pens

Session 5: Notes - The Gifts Of The Holy Spirit

Bible Passage: 1 Corinthians 12:27-31
It's helpful for each member of the group to have a Bible as well as a workbook.

 Connect

Play 'Pass the parcel'.

You will need:
Music
Wrapping paper and gifts
Paper and pens

Prepare ahead a parcel with enough layers for each person to have a turn. Between each layer you could put a wrapped sweet or chocolate bar. Also, put the name of one gift of Holy Spirit between each layer. You could ask people to read it out and maybe tell a story they've heard about someone using it or an experience they've had. You might want to put a bigger prize in the last layer to be unwrapped.

There are nine gifts that most people will be familiar with from 1 Corinthians 12.

Word of Wisdom
Word of Knowledge
Faith
Gifts of Healing
Working of Miracles

Prophecy
Discerning of Spirits
Tongues
Interpretation of Tongues

But there are some other really important gifts that may be neglected or may not be seen as spiritual (there are some listed in Ephesians 4:11-12).

Helping
Administration
Ministry/Service
Teaching
Encouragement
Giving

Leadership
Mercy
Apostleship
Evangelism
Pastoral Guidance

Eat It Up

Word of wisdom: The ability to be able to make decisions and give guidance in line with God's will.

Word of knowledge: Knowledge and understanding about things, founded in the gospel and related to Scripture. The ability to tell others this knowledge, in certain situations.

Faith: The ability to trust in God in difficult or seemingly impossible situations and trust that God will accomplish what needs to be done.

Gifts of healing: The ability to pray for the sick and to trust God to heal them through supernatural means.

Working of miracles: Trusting God to show up in supernatural ways and see the uncommon happen.

Prophecy: Hearing from God and communicating what he has said to others.

Discerning of Spirits: To perceive atmospheres and to evaluate situations or people and know where their influence is coming from.

Tongues: Speaking in other languages or heavenly languages.

Interpretation of tongues: A translation of a word given in tongues.

Administration: Someone who is able to guide and direct a group of people towards a goal or a destination. It means people are able to organise, strategise and implement plans and lead others.

Mercy: Ability to be compassionate, have empathy for and patience towards those who are afflicted or suffering in any way.

And the lists in the Bible aren't exhaustive – there are plenty of other gifts of the Spirit which God in his grace is longing to give us!

Give It Up

You may want to put some music on and encourage people to be bold in speaking out. You could take it in turns to stand in the middle of the group while the others thank God for different things about that person.

Over The Edge

You will need:
Paper and pens
Hat or bowl

Session 6: Notes - Holy Spirit Working In Us And Through Us

Bible Passage: Acts 16:6-10
It's helpful for each member of the group to have a Bible as well as a workbook.

Connect

Play the Blindfold Shape Drawing Challenge.

You will need:
Blindfolds
Paper and pens

In pairs, one person is blindfolded and the other person draws a series of three shapes on a sheet of paper. He/she then describes the shapes to the blindfolded person and where the shapes/lines are placed on the paper. The blindfolded person attempts to draw the same shapes just from the description. The idea is that when the blindfold is removed the two pieces of paper should look exactly the same.

Creating Space

It is possible that we could be fearful that if we allow Holy Spirit to work in and through us, we will be asked to do something we have never wanted to do. I think it is helpful to note that our healthy desires are God-given and as Holy Spirit fills us, actually we see our natural abilities come alive and flourish.

Often the beginning of our transformation is that we are free to be who God made us to be and the urge to be like someone else stops. The comparison of ourselves to other people stops. The voices in our head that we are not and never will be good enough, stop.

Total transformation happens as we discover, through both the Word of God and our filling from Holy Spirit, our true identity and our God-given purpose.

Our pursuit of Holy Spirit cannot be a pursuit for his power alone. Holy Spirit power is to bring us, and the people around us, into an encounter with the Father.

To truly live in the fullness of God talked about in Ephesians 3 we need both the Word of God and his power. If we pursue one and not the other we miss the point – intimacy with God.

Oswald Chambers wrote in his book, *'My Utmost For His Highest'*:

"It's a joy to Jesus when a person takes time to walk more intimately with him. The bearing of fruit is always shown in Scripture to be a visible result of an intimate relationship with Jesus Christ."

 ## Eat It Up

You may want to ask people to look up these verses and talk together about the supernatural being released in the natural.

Although God doesn't like sickness or disease, we live in a fallen world. Jesus is clearly against sickness and disorder in this world, and Holy Spirit fills us with power to overcome the atmosphere instead of coming under it.

 ## Give It Up

You might want to put some background music on. Give people a little time to connect with God and dare them to dream. It is OK to engage your imagination seeing as it is God-given. Then encourage them to let those God-given desires expand and increase.

Recommended Books For Further Study

Encounter the Holy Spirit - Jeannie Morgan
True stories, biblical accounts and practical steps to getting filled and empowered by the Holy Spirit.
Publisher: Monarch Books
ISBN: 978-0857211682

Forgotten God - Francis Chan
Reversing our tragic neglect of the Holy Spirit.
Publisher: David C Cook
ISBN: 978-1434767950

Hosting The Presence - Bill Johnson
Unveiling Heaven's agenda.
Publisher: Destiny Image Publishers
ISBN: 978-0768441291

Power Evangelism - John Wimber
Learn to become more effective in evangelism and see the Spirit of God work in power. Includes study guide.
Publisher: Hodder & Stoughton
ISBN: 978-1444750270

Red Moon Rising - Pete Greig
How 24-7 Prayer Is Awakening A Generation
Publisher: David C Cook
ISBN: 978-1434708908

The Spirit-Filled Church - Terry Virgo
Finding your place in God's purpose.
Publisher: Monarch Books
ISBN: 978-0857210494

OTHER TITLES IN THE SPRING HARVEST BIBLE STUDIES SERIES:

Daniel – Faith Under Fire
Daniel's faith was literally tested by fire, but his God – and our God – proves himself faithful in the most extreme of situations.
SHB1351B

Passion – Finding An Unshakeable Hope
Exploring the significance of the cross and resurrection for our lives, hopes and relationships will help us grow in confidence and in the character and grace of God.
SHB1319B

Yahweh – God In All His Fullness
7 studies which seek to guide you into a deeper grasp of the magnificence of God.
SHB1389B

Malachi - Wholehearted
Reflections on worship, justice and the faithfulness of God
SHB1639B

Ephesians - United
6 sessions that reflect on the church and living a Christ-inspired lifestyle.
SHB1739B

1 John
Get close to the Source in being, saying and doing.
SHB1839B

Romans 8 - Inseparable
Life in Christ, in the Spirit, and in the World
SHB1351B